Create beautiful, lifelike artwork
that is uniquely yours.

Immerse yourself in the space between black and white and explore the many shades of your imagination.

Helpful hints to optimize your coloring experience:

 Using the gray as your guide, you will feel like a professional artist, bringing depth and color to each image and creating lifelike artwork that is uniquely yours.

1. Color over the areas with the heaviest gray shading, using your darkest colors.

2. Color over the areas with the lightest gray shading, using your palest colors.

3. Color over the remaining areas using your medium colors to seamlessly blend light and dark.

Watch as your beautiful creature emerges from the grayscale!

Beautiful
CREATURES

A BOUNDLESS COLORING BOOK ADVENTURE

Huelish
www.huelish.com

Distributed in Canada by Raincoast Books
2440 Viking Way   Richmond, BC   Canada, V6V 1N2

Cataloguing data available from Library and Archives Canada

ISBN 978-0-9948623-0-3 (paperback)

Book design by Elisa Gutiérrez
Cover art by Nicole Stocker
Photographs sourced from Pixabay

FSC
www.fsc.org
MIX
Paper from
responsible sources
FSC® C016245

Printed and bound in Canada by
Friesens on FSC certified paper
which ensures that products come
from responsibly managed forests.

16 17 18 19   5 4 3 2

NICOLE STOCKER

Beautiful
CREATURES

A BOUNDLESS COLORING BOOK ADVENTURE

Color over the gray to bring your image to life

HUELISH

*A*s children, we were naturally drawn to the simple joy and comfort of coloring. Putting crayon to paper (or walls!) was an instinctive form of creative expression, long abandoned by our serious adult selves. *Beautiful Creatures* invites you to return to the peaceful world of coloring, where the thrill of fresh colors on crisp paper awaits.

Simply color over the gray, matching light and dark tones to reveal lifelike shading. Saturate the grayscale with heavy color, use the lightest of touches, or simply let it be. Whether you flood the page with vibrant brights or a softer color palette emerges, as the artist-in-residence there are no limits to what you can create.

Printed on acid-free, archival quality paper, perforated for framing, each creation is a deliciously tactile experience that will make you feel like a true artist. Disconnect from the intensity of everyday life, sink into a meditative state, and watch as the striking monochrome images come to life with color. *Beautiful Creatures* is a soothing elixir for a case of chronic adulthood.

Nicole Stocker

— Enjoy!

ARTWORK

by

_____

COMPLETED ON

ARTWORK
by

COMPLETED ON

ARTWORK by

COMPLETED ON

ARTWORK
by

COMPLETED ON

ARTWORK
by

COMPLETED ON

ARTWORK

by

COMPLETED ON

ARTWORK
by

COMPLETED ON

ARTWORK

by

COMPLETED ON

ARTWORK by

COMPLETED ON

ARTWORK
by

COMPLETED ON

ARTWORK

by

COMPLETED ON

ARTWORK

by

COMPLETED ON

ARTWORK
by

COMPLETED ON

ARTWORK

by

COMPLETED ON

ARTWORK

by

COMPLETED ON

ARTWORK
by

COMPLETED ON

ARTWORK
by

COMPLETED ON

ARTWORK
by

COMPLETED ON

ARTWORK

by

COMPLETED ON

ARTWORK
by

COMPLETED ON

ARTWORK

by

COMPLETED ON

ARTWORK
by

COMPLETED ON

ARTWORK by

COMPLETED ON

ARTWORK

by

COMPLETED ON

ARTWORK
by

COMPLETED ON

ARTWORK

by

COMPLETED ON

ARTWORK *by*

COMPLETED ON

ARTWORK
by

COMPLETED ON

ARTWORK

by

COMPLETED ON

ARTWORK
by

COMPLETED ON

ARTWORK

by

COMPLETED ON

ARTWORK

by

COMPLETED ON

ARTWORK by

COMPLETED ON

ARTWORK *by*

COMPLETED ON

ARTWORK

by

COMPLETED ON

ARTWORK

by

COMPLETED ON

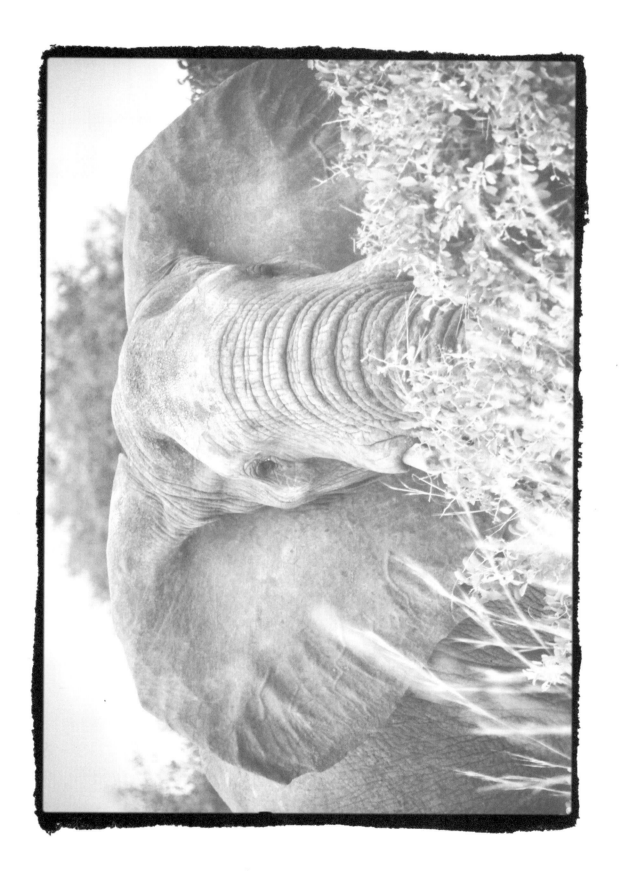

ARTWORK *by*

COMPLETED ON

ARTWORK
by

COMPLETED ON

ARTWORK
by

COMPLETED ON

ARTWORK

by

COMPLETED ON

ARTWORK *by*

COMPLETED ON

ARTWORK

by

COMPLETED ON

ARTWORK by

COMPLETED ON

ARTWORK *by*

COMPLETED ON

ARTWORK
by

COMPLETED ON

ARTWORK
by

COMPLETED ON

ARTWORK
by

COMPLETED ON

ARTWORK

by

COMPLETED ON

As a young girl, Nicole was enchanted by a black and white photograph hanging in her parents' summer cabin, wishing she could bring it to life with color. An artist at heart, Nicole imagined a collection of coloring books filled with inspiring, carefully curated photographs. The first in a series, *Beautiful Creatures* marks her publishing debut. A mother of two young children, Nicole treasures any moment to lose herself in color and creation in her Vancouver home.

Share your artwork. See what others are creating.

HUELISH

www.huelish.com

@huelish

Thank you for taking part in this coloring adventure.
Until the next one . . .

Nicole Stocker